*CRI...

Ro...

SANTA SCAM

illustrated by Kevin Hopgood

W
FRANKLIN WATTS
LONDON•SYDNEY

First published in 2007 by
Franklin Watts
338 Euston Road
London NW1 3BH

Franklin Watts Australia
Level 17/207 Kent Street
Sydney NSW 2000

A CIP catalogue record for this book
is available from the British Library.

ISBN: 978 0 7496 7056 6

Dewey Classification Number: 823.914

Illustrator: Kevin Hopgood
Series editor: Adrian Cole
Reading consultant: Prue Goodwin, Lecturer at the
National Centre for Language and Literacy, Reading
Art director and cover designer: Jonathan Hair

Cover photo: Adrian Cole

Printed in Great Britain by Bookmarque Ltd

Franklin Watts is a division of
Hachette Children's Books.

A note from the author:
Crime Files are true
stories, but some of
the events on which
they are based have
been dramatised
and edited.

Contents

1: Shiny, red Jaguar

It was late November and the winter sunshine beat down on a luxury car showroom in Miami, Florida, USA.

Inside the showroom everything smelled of polish and new leather. A cheerful, sun-tanned salesman was explaining the wonders of the latest Jaguar XK8 to a customer.

'It'll do 0–60 in 4.9 seconds,' he said.

'Is this the top of the range model?' the customer asked. He was wearing a designer suit and a silk shirt, but there was something about the guy that made the salesman think he wasn't a serious buyer. He just didn't look like he had the money to buy the expensive car he was now sitting in.

'The top of the range model is on the other side of the showroom, sir,' the salesman said. 'It comes with a 6-speaker stereo system, wood and leather steering wheel and 20-inch alloy wheels.'

'That's the one for me!' said the customer.

The salesman looked hard at the customer. He was certain this guy was a joker, someone who liked to sit in luxury cars, but had no way of actually buying one.

'It's got a price tag of $81,500,' the salesman pointed out.

'It's still the car for me,' said the customer. 'Now, where do I sign?'

The salesman led the customer over to a small desk at the back of the showroom.

'Can I get you a cup of coffee?' he asked.

The customer shook his head. 'No thanks, just show me where to sign,' he replied with a laugh.

Finally, the salesman returned with the sales papers. He still had an uneasy feeling, but when the customer took out his pen to sign, he saw a very expensive-looking watch on his wrist. About $5,000 worth of watch. The salesman breathed a sigh of relief. Obviously, if this guy had enough money to buy a $5,000 watch, he could afford a Jaguar XK8.

The customer handed over a cheque
for $81,500. The salesman read the
signature: David Ellisor. 'What line of
business are you in, Mr Ellisor?' he asked.

'Me? Oh, I arrange concerts and events,'
replied David Ellisor with a sly smile.
'And as you can see, my line of business
is doing well. Very well indeed.'

'Well, I hope you enjoy your new car, sir,' said the salesman. 'And have a merry Christmas.'

'Oh, I will,' said David Ellisor, with a smirk. His eyes flickered towards a large poster in the showroom window. It advertised Miami's *Christmas from Around the World Spectacular* at the Coconut Grove Expo Centre. 'Oh yes, I'm going to have myself a very merry Christmas!'

2: Christmas promise

I thought Christmas in our family was going to be different this year. For the last two years, since Dad left, things had been pretty tough at home. In fact, I don't think my kid brother Mikey had really known a proper Christmas. But that was soon going to change.

Mom had managed to save a bit of extra money over the year, and I had earned a few dollars doing odd jobs down at the grocery mart on Saturdays. This meant we could afford to buy a couple of tickets for me to take Mikey to the big Christmas Spectacular at the Coconut Grove Expo Centre on South Bayshore Drive.

Everyone was talking about it. But the tickets didn't come cheap: $10 for Mikey; $30 for me because I was older.

'It's a lot of money, Mom,' I said.

'Sure Jason, but just look at what you're getting. Mikey will love it!' She flashed me a wide grin. 'And, if the truth be told, I bet you will too, honey.'

I had another look through the glossy Christmas Spectacular brochure. There were going to be Christmas trees and lights, a stage show, a Christmas dinner, a treasure hunt with a gift for everyone, mystery guests including a Harry Potter lookalike and ambassadors from 28 different countries. The promoter said there had never been an event like it.

The morning I showed Mikey the tickets, I thought he would explode with excitement!

'This is going to be the best Christmas ever!' he declared.

From then on, Mikey didn't stop talking about the Christmas Spectacular. We heard how everybody in his grade was going. And we heard how the school was holding a cake sale to raise money for those kids whose parents couldn't afford tickets. Mikey and his friends spent all their time talking about the bits they were looking forward to most.

'The treasure hunt!' shouted Jamie-Lee.

'No, the stage show!' screamed Mary-Beth.

'I just want to see Santa Claus,' said Mikey.

The night before the show Mikey was so excited I don't think he slept a wink. To be honest, even though I tried not to show it, I was excited too. Well, who wouldn't be? As the show's promoter said, this was going to be a once-in-a-lifetime experience.

3: Show time

It was the first time I've ever known Mikey to be ready early for school.

'Hurry up, Jason!' he yelled. 'We'll miss the bus!'

At the school gates, everyone clambered onto the buses. People were wearing Santa hats or plastic reindeer antlers, or had tinsel in their hair. There was so much excitement about. Even the teachers were smiling.

On the bus, everybody joined in the
Christmas songs. We sang 'Rudolph the
Red-Nosed Reindeer', 'Jingle Bells' and
'Frosty the Snowman' again and again
and again.

As the bus turned into the Expo Centre car park, we could see that lots of other buses full of kids had already parked up. By the time the last bus arrived, the parking lot was jam-packed.

'It's amazing!' one of Mikey's teachers said to me. 'There must be over 2,500 kids here. It should be a really great show, what with Santa Claus and the Christmas dinner and the treasure hunt... never mind the kids, I'm looking forward to it all myself!'

'Me, too!' I said.

'What time do the doors open?' asked one of the other teachers.

'Don't know, any moment soon I should think,' came the reply.

As we waited in the warm sunshine, the kids all looked around to see who would be first to spot Santa Claus arriving on his sleigh.

'When does it start?' asked Mikey, tugging my arm.

I glanced at my watch. Quarter past ten. The show had been due to start fifteen minutes ago.

'They must be behind schedule getting set up,' I said. But something was bugging me. On the walls there were lots of posters advertising various shows at the centre, but none for the Christmas Spectacular. It was as though it wasn't happening.

At half past ten the kids were getting
fidgety. There were worried looks on the
faces of the adults. A couple of teachers
started hammering on the bolted doors,
but there was no answer.

I took out our tickets, just to make sure
that somehow 2,500 of us hadn't got the
date wrong. We hadn't. There was a
phone number on the ticket. With a
sickening feeling in my stomach, I flipped
up the top of my cell phone and dialled.

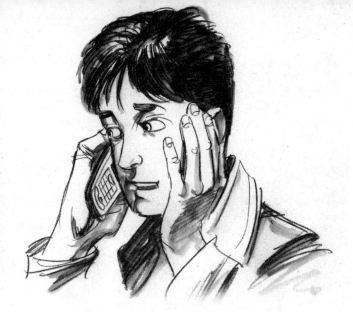

There was a recorded message. 'Hi!' it
said. 'The Christmas Spectacular has
been cancelled. We're very sorry. Bye!'

'What's it say, Jason?' Mikey asked me,
excitedly.

I didn't say anything. I didn't need to.
Mikey could see the tears welling up
in my eyes.

They were tears of anger.

4: A swift getaway

'Cancelled?' one teacher said.

'I feel so stupid' said another teacher. 'How can we all have been conned so easily?'

Word spread through the waiting children, teachers and helpers like wildfire. Kids started crying and yelling. Teachers started shouting; using words that I would have got a detention for saying.

Mikey was sobbing his heart out. I put an arm round his shoulders and pulled him to me. I felt pretty sick about things myself. All the money I'd worked so hard to earn; and all of Mom's savings, gone straight into some conman's pocket.

This crook was a bully as well as a thief. He hadn't picked on people his own size to rob; he'd picked on kids – and at Christmas.

I led Mikey over to the edge of
the parking lot, where it was
quieter. I couldn't believe what
was happening. I peered through
the wire fence and watched the
cars racing by on South Bayshore
Drive. My eye was caught by a
shiny car parked up at the side
of the road. I like fast cars and
I knew that the car wasn't an
American model. It was sleek,
bright red – and brand new.
It was a Jaguar XK8.

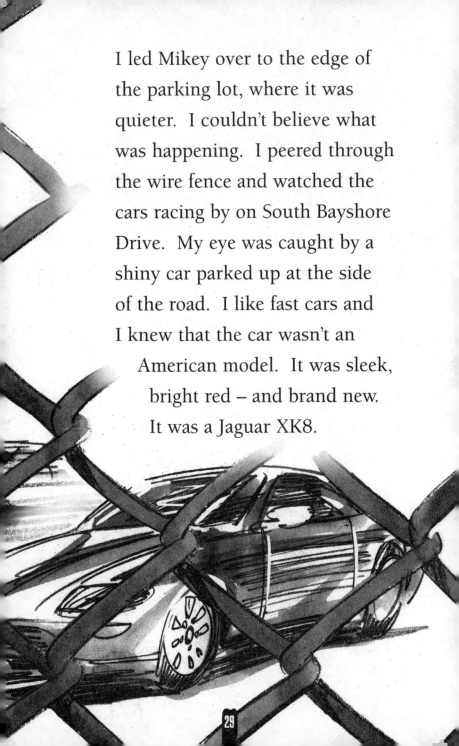

As I stared at the side window of the
car, I saw that the driver was looking
at Mikey and me. His face spread into
a wide grin, and he put up his arm in
a kind of wave. Then he sped off down
South Bayshore Drive.

I'd seen him before at our school. He
was the promoter who had taken our
money. The man who had stolen
Mikey's – and thousands of other kids' –
Christmas. And I was going to do
my best to make sure he paid them
back one way or another.

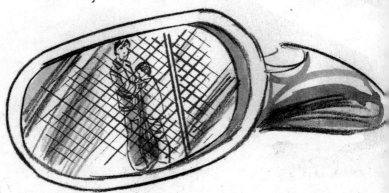

5: Hot pursuit

By now the cops had arrived and were talking to some of the teachers.

I grabbed Mikey's hand and pushed my way furiously through the crowds of crying children and angry teachers and helpers.

'Excuse me!' I said to the officer who seemed to be in charge, but he didn't hear me. He was too busy trying to talk to the teachers. He wasn't bothered with a kid like me.

'Any idea who we are looking for here, ma'am?' the officer asked one of the teachers.

'Yes sir, I have!' I shouted. And this time the officer heard me.

I told him about the man Mikey and I
had seen watching the Coconut Grove,
who I had recognised as the promoter.

'Can you describe him?' asked the officer.

'Yep. Mousy, straggly blond hair. Driving
a brand new, bright red Jaguar XK8.'

'Not too many of those in Miami,' said the officer. 'With a bit of luck, and thanks to your help, we'll get this son of a Grinch!'

I just hoped against hope that he would. Not for my sake though, but for Mikey's and all the other kids whose Christmas he had ruined.

6: The net closes

The phone in the Jaguar showroom rang.
The car salesman picked it up. 'Hello?'
He listened to a voice on the other end.

'Yes, officer. We've sold a red Jaguar
XK8 recently.' He opened his file of sales
orders. 'To a Mr David Ellisor, staying at
the Hotel Paradiso.'

Shortly after at the Hotel Paradiso, the two police officers waited impatiently as the receptionist held a telephone to her ear.

'I'm sorry, officer,' she said, eventually. 'There's no answer from Mr Ellisor's room.'

'Dang! We've lost him!' muttered the
senior officer. Suddenly, his police
radio crackled to life. 'Yeah. Uh-huh!'
He turned to his colleague. 'That was
Highway Patrol. A red Jaguar XK8 has
been spotted, heading towards the
airport. Let's go!'

'Here's your ticket, Mr Ellisor,' said the girl at the airport ticket desk. 'Are you taking your bag into the cabin with you?'

'You bet I am!' said David Ellisor.
He wasn't going to tell the girl, but
it contained $20,000 in cash.

A voice over the tannoy announced the next flight: 'Flight AE3401 to Bermuda is now boarding at Gate 3.'

'That's my flight!' said David Ellisor.

'Have a good Christmas!' said the girl at the desk.

'I certainly will!' said David Ellisor.

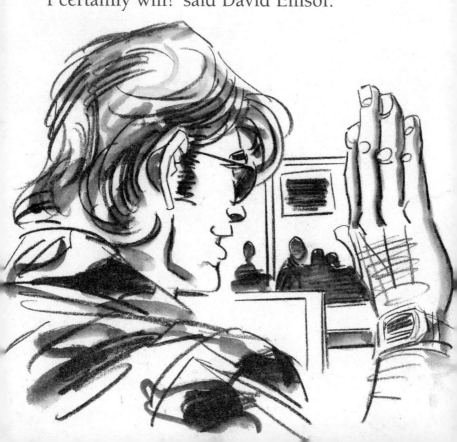

'Oh no you won't!' a voice growled behind him.

David Ellisor spun round and found himself facing the two officers from the Miami Police Department.

The crook who had stolen Christmas wasn't going anywhere – except to jail.

i: Crime Files appendix

* The investigation

The investigation into the Santa scam was made by a team from the Federal Bureau of Investigation (FBI), and headed by Special Agent Michael S. Clemens. According to the FBI, David Ellisor had carried out similar scams in the states of Utah, California, Missouri, Colorado and Arizona. They also discovered Ellisor had used the money from the scam to fund his rich lifestyle, including expensive dinners, a luxury hotel suite, a gold watch and a new Jaguar car.

* The trial

The trial of David Ellisor took place in Miami, Florida, in February 2005. He was found guilty on eight counts of mail fraud, for a scam which involved selling more than 2,700 show tickets. Of course, the event never took place. Ellisor was sentenced to 87 months in prison and ordered to repay $38,000.

* In defence

According to reports from the trial, Ellisor told the jury that on the day the show was to take place he sat in his car, opposite the Coconut Grove Expo Centre. After everyone had arrived Ellisor said he intended to explain to the teachers and parents. He also said he wanted to reschedule the show, but had been scared off when he saw the angry reaction of some people.

* Final word

One report in the *Miami Herald* declared after the trial: 'Now the Grinch has had his day in court, and the justice system has spoken'.

ii: Word file

Ambassadors – people who visit a different country to represent their own country.

Cell phone – a mobile phone.

Crook – a word sometimes used to describe a thief or dishonest person.

Grinch – a word, taken from books by Dr Seuss, used to describe someone who is mean and unpleasant.

Grocery mart – a shop selling food.

Highway Patrol – U.S. police who patrol the roads in cars or on motorcycles.

Jury – a group of 12 people in a court of law who decide whether someone is guilty or not guilty of a crime.

Mail fraud – the use of the U.S. mail service to steal money from people.

Promoter – someone who organises events.

Top of the range – the best of a group.

Wildfire – a phrase describing something that moves quickly, like wildfire that burns through a forest.

iii: Crime Files weblinks

http://www.fbi.gov/page2/dec05/
holidayscam120505.htm

This is an archive page from the Federal
Bureau of Investigation website. It describes
the story of 'the crook who stole Christmas'.

http://www.usdoj.gov/usao/fls/
PressReleases/050810-05.html

This press release is on the website of the
U.S. Department of Justice. It was issued
following the sentencing of David Ellisor.

http://www.sptimes.com/2003/12/05/
State/Christmas_show_is_a_G.shtml

This is an archive news page on the
St Petersburg Times online website.
It covers the Santa scam story.

http://www.fbi.gov/fbikids.htm

A kids' website from the FBI, featuring
games and stories, and introducing a
glimpse at the way the FBI works.

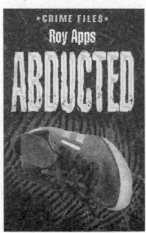